RACE to a New START

Printed in the United States of America
ISBN: (paperback): 978-1-7371726-0-4
ISBN: (hardback): 978-1-7371726-1-1
ISBN: (ebook): 978-1-7371726-2-8

Dedicated to everyone who will read this book and to all the children to whom we entrust the future

Martin and Malcolm have been friends for as long as they can remember. They both want to be track stars when they get older and go to the park to run against each other every chance they get.

Today is just like any other day!
RACE DAY!
The other kids are standing around in the park waiting for the showdown. Michelle uses her outside voice and says, "On Your Mark! Get Set! Go!" Martin and Malcolm take off running as fast as they can.

Half way through the race, Martin passes Malcolm running even faster and Malcolm is having a hard time keeping up. Martin wins the race and everyone is cheering for him.

When Malcolm crosses the finish line, he is huffing and puffing really loudly. Martin turns to Malcolm and says, "Are you okay? You look like you are about pass out!" Malcolm replies, "I'm out of breath. How are you able to run so fast all the time? I can't keep up like I used to!"

"I follow these 8 rules that my dad told me about," Martin says.
"And they make you run that fast? I want to know about these rules!" Malcolm exclaims.
Everyone else chimes in and wants to learn about the rules that have Martin running like he is the fastest boy on earth.

A.R.T

Martin speaks up so everyone can hear him. "The rules are an acronym for the words NEW START." Andrew screams out from the back of the crowd, "What is an acronym?"

Nutrition

Martin continues, "An acronym is a word where the letters stand for the first letters of other words."

Michelle says, "I'm not sure I understand what you mean."

Martin responds, "Alright, let me break it down for you guys. Our acronym is NEW START.

N stands for Nutrition.

For us to be nutritious, we must pay attention to what we eat."

"You know how we like to eat candy, chips, fast food and drink soda?" Martin asks.

Everybody replies, "YES!"

"Well," Martin says, "Those things are not good for our bodies."

"So what can we eat?" Malcolm asks.

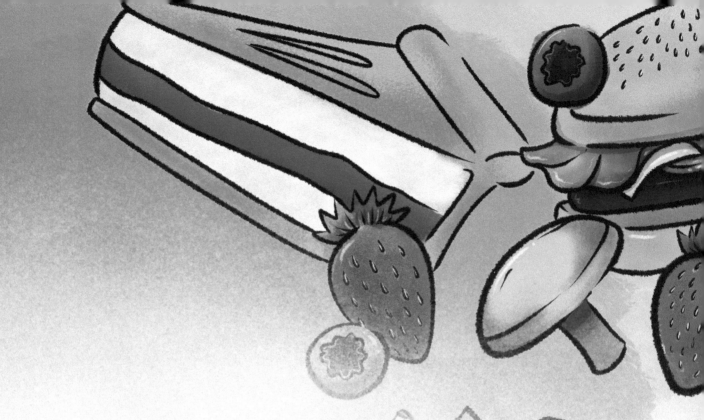

"We have to try our best to eat fruits, vegetables, proteins and grains," Martin says.

"My parents tell me to eat those all the time! They don't taste good," Malcolm exclaims.

"It doesn't taste that good at first, but that's only because you're not used to it. The healthy foods help our bodies have more energy. That's how I got fast! You have to try it out," Martin says.

"Alright, I will think about it," Malcolm agrees.

"What's the next one?" Michelle asks.

"The next one is E which stands for **Exercise**. Exercise means moving around for at least 30 minutes a day," Martin responds.

"But where can we exercise like that?" asks Andrew.

Michelle bursts out and asks, "What about playing in the park, or in the yard, or going swimming?"

Martin replies, "You're right! Fresh air, even after rain or snow, is always good!"

Exercise

"W comes next and it stands for Water," Martin continues.

"I drink water every day so I'm good, right?" asks Malcolm.

"Drinking water every day is good, but we have to drink about 7-9 cups a day," Martin replies.

"What about my parents and my little brother?" Malcolm asks.

"My mom and dad drink 8-10 cups a day and my little sister drinks about 6-7 cups a day," says Martin.

"Why do we need to drink so much water?" Andrew asks.

"Because our bodies are made up of mostly water, we need to make sure we are replacing the water that leaves our bodies everyday as well as getting rid of all the bad stuff inside us," Martin responds.

"Wow, I've never heard that before!" Michelle exclaims.

unshine

"S stands for Sunshine," Martin says.
"Do we have to stand in the sun?" asks
Malcolm.
"Pretty much! Sunlight gives us Vitamin D which
our bodies need," Martin replies. "What happens if I
can't go outside to get any sun?" Andrew asks.

"Letting sunlight through the windows or the doors is better than no sunlight at all. My dad says Vitamin D levels are important to keep our bones, teeth, and muscles healthy and strong," Martin says.
"That's so cool!" Everyone exclaims in unison.

"T is next! What does it stand for?" Michelle asks.
"T stands for Temperance. Temperance means to stay away from things that are bad for you, but have some limits on the things that are good for you. We should avoid using things that are harmful and do damage to our bodies," Martin says.
"What are some of the good stuff we can have some limits on?" Malcolm wonders aloud.

mperance

"We can be temperate in our eating habits. Instead of eating late at night or whenever we feel like it, we should be eating heavy at breakfast time, medium at lunch time, and light at dinner time," Martin says.
"Why?" Michelle asks.
"The closer to bedtime we eat, the more work we give our bodies while we are sleeping," Martin replies.

Martin continues, "Rather than actually resting, our bodies spend the night digesting food."
"I wonder if my dad knows this! He has midnight snacks ALL the time!" Andrew exclaims.
Martin chuckles and says, "Maybe he doesn't, but you should tell him when you get home."

"A stands for Air," Martin says.
"Well, what about air?" Malcolm asks.
"During the day, we have to make sure to breathe deeply to get all the oxygen into our lungs. Exercising in the open air helps the good air get into our bodies," Martin replies.

We have to stand and sit up straight to help more air get into our lungs to help us breathe better," Martin continues.
"So like this?" Malcolm tries to take a really deep breath!
"Just like that!" Martin says with a really big smile on his face.

"We're almost done guys!" Martin says.

"Good!" Malcolm replies, "You know our parents want us home before the streetlights come on."

"Next is R," Martin continues. "R is for Rest!"

"How much rest do we need? My bedtime is 8pm," says Andrew.

"Kids our age need to sleep for 10-12 hours," Martin replies.

Rest

Martin continues, "We need rest to help us have a lot of energy for the next day."
"Is that why our parents send us to bed so early?" Michelle asks.
"I would like to believe so!" Martin responds.

"We're on the last one! What is it? What is it?" Andrew asks excitedly.

"The last T stands for Trust in God," Martin says.

"And what does that mean?" Andrew asks.

"I'll try to explain it the best way I know how," Martin replies.

"We trust in a lot of things everyday without realizing it. We trust that the car our parents drive will take us to our destination without breaking down. We trust that our parents will provide us with Nutritious food, clothes to Exercise, Water to drink, sunglasses in the Sunshine, toys for us to be Temperate with..."

Trust

"I see where you are going with this," Michelle says. "We really do trust our parents with our lives every day." "That's right! We can trust God in the same way because He cares about us and wants the best for us," Martin replies.

"And if I trust in God, will it help me run faster?" Malcolm asks. Martin answers, "If you trust in God to help you with anything, He will help you." "God sounds pretty cool!" Malcolm exclaims.

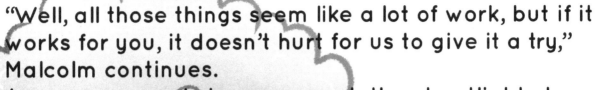

"Well, all those things seem like a lot of work, but if it works for you, it doesn't hurt for us to give it a try," Malcolm continues.

As everyone nods in agreement, the streetlights turn on.

"Oh no! The streetlights are on! Let's Go!!!" Martin screams.

Everyone hops on their bikes and begin to hurry home.

The

Malcolm turns to Martin and says, "I'll race you to our block!"

Martin says, "You're on!"

Author's Note

My name is Chinyere Nwaoha, or ChiChi, for short. I am a New York City based entrepreneur and children's book author.

My inspiration to write this book came from my love for being healthy and my mom's career as a dietitian/nutritionist. Being able to share health and lifestyle principles with the world brings joy to my heart.

I hope you and your family enjoyed reading this book as much as I enjoyed writing it for you.

For more information about the author, visit her website at www.gethealthywithchichi.com.

CPSIA information can be obtained
at www.ICGtesting.com
Printed in the USA
BVHW021938101121
621200BV00001B/5